Sadlier

We◦Believe™

Review & Resource Book

Project Director
Kathleen Hendricks

Contributing Writer
John Stack

Grade Four

Sadlier
A Division of William H. Sadlier, Inc.

Welcome to the **Grade 4** *We Believe* **Review & Resource Book.**

The activities in this book are designed to be used with the core chapters in the Grade 4 *We Believe* textbook.

Included are questions that will help you remember what has been learned, ideas for prayer and reflection, and suggestions for living the faith in everyday life. Some activities are suggested to be completed with a parent or other family member.

For additional ideas, activities, and opportunities:

Visit Sadlier's

www.WE BELIEVE web.com

Nihil Obstat
✠ Most Reverend Robert C. Morlino

Imprimatur
✠ Most Reverend Robert C. Morlino
Bishop of Madison
April 29, 2004

The *Nihil Obstat* and *Imprimatur* are official declarations that a book or pamphlet is free of doctrinal or moral error. No implication is contained therein that those who have granted the *Nihil Obstat* and *Imprimatur* agree with the contents, opinions, or statements expressed.

S is a registered trademark of William H. Sadlier, Inc.
WE BELIEVE™ is a registered trademark of William H. Sadlier, Inc.

William H. Sadlier, Inc.
9 Pine Street
New York, NY 10005-1002

ISBN: 978-0-8215-5424-7
13 14 15 16 WEBC 15 14 13 12 11

Contents

CORE CHAPTERS

Jesus—the Way, the Truth, and the Life

Remember

The name of Jesus means "God saves." God had a special mission for his Son. This mission of Jesus Christ is to save us. In the space design a card in praise of Jesus, thanking him for coming into the world to show us the way to the Father. Use one or more of these images of Jesus to decorate your card:

I am the Bread of Life.

I am the Light of the World.

I am the Good Shepherd.

I am the Resurrection and the Life.

I am the Way and the Truth and the Life.

You might want to use your design as a basis for a larger card that you and your class can present to your parish for use at a liturgy.

Key Words

Follow the road to knowing Jesus by using these words on the stepping stones.

Incarnation

disciples

Original Sin

blessed

grace

Blessed Trinity

sin

Savior

Church

START

The

is the truth that the Son of God became man.

Those who said "yes" to Jesus' call and followed him were his

The Three Persons in One God: God the Father, God the Son, and God the Holy Spirit is the

is the first sin committed by the first human beings.

is the title given to Jesus because he died and rose to save us from sin.

The gift of God's life in us is called

FINISH

The

is the community of people who are baptized and follow Jesus Christ.

Reflect & Pray

Jesus promised that the Father would send the Holy Spirit. The Holy Spirit helped the disciples to remember and believe all that Jesus told them.

Complete this prayer to the Holy Spirit with a partner or family member.

Just Say "Yes" Prayer

Holy Spirit, help me to become a twenty-first-century disciple by saying "yes" to Jesus.

At home when I _____

_____.

At school when I _____

_____.

In my parish when I _____

_____.

With friends when I _____

_____.

Holy Spirit, guide me through each day as I say "yes" to Jesus' call to follow him. Amen.

Make a copy of your prayer, and put it in a place where you will see it each day.

Our Catholic Life

Think of someone in your parish, school, neighborhood, town, or city who does a great job of spreading the Good News about Jesus in words or in actions. Write a short speech nominating this disciple for a special award.

The Good News Award Nomination

I nominate _____
for a Good News Award.

I selected _____

because _____

_____

_____.

When you finish, choose one of these ways to follow through with your nomination:

- Write to that person about his or her nomination. He or she may be very happy to hear from you.

- Invite that person to come to your class or group to receive a special thank you.

- You might want to plan an awards ceremony to honor the people who are nominated by the class.

Report what you did here.

_____

_____

_____

_____

_____

Jesus Leads Us to Happiness

Remember

The Beatitudes are teachings of Jesus that describe the way to live as his disciples. Read the list of Beatitudes in your *We Believe* text. Choose one and write it here.

_____

_____

_____

Talk about ways your parish helps people live this Beatitude. (Clue: Check your parish bulletin or Web site for ideas.)

Key Words

What if you were an online newspaper reporter who was assigned to cover the story of Jesus teaching his disciples? Write a short article about what Jesus said and how the disciples reacted. Use these **Key Words** in your article.

> **peace**
> **Beatitudes**
> **Kingdom of God**
> **justice**
> **mission**

We Believe

Address: www.webelieveweb.com

_____

_____

_____

_____

_____

_____

Reflect & Pray

Jesus prayed in different ways. He prayed when he was alone, and he prayed with his disciples and with the people in his community.

When do you like to pray by yourself?

_____

_____

_____

When do you pray with others?

_____

_____

_____

No matter what is happening in our lives, Jesus wants us to trust in God's love as he did. Write your own prayer asking for God's help in your life.

_____

_____

_____

_____

_____

_____

_____

_____

_____

_____

_____

_____

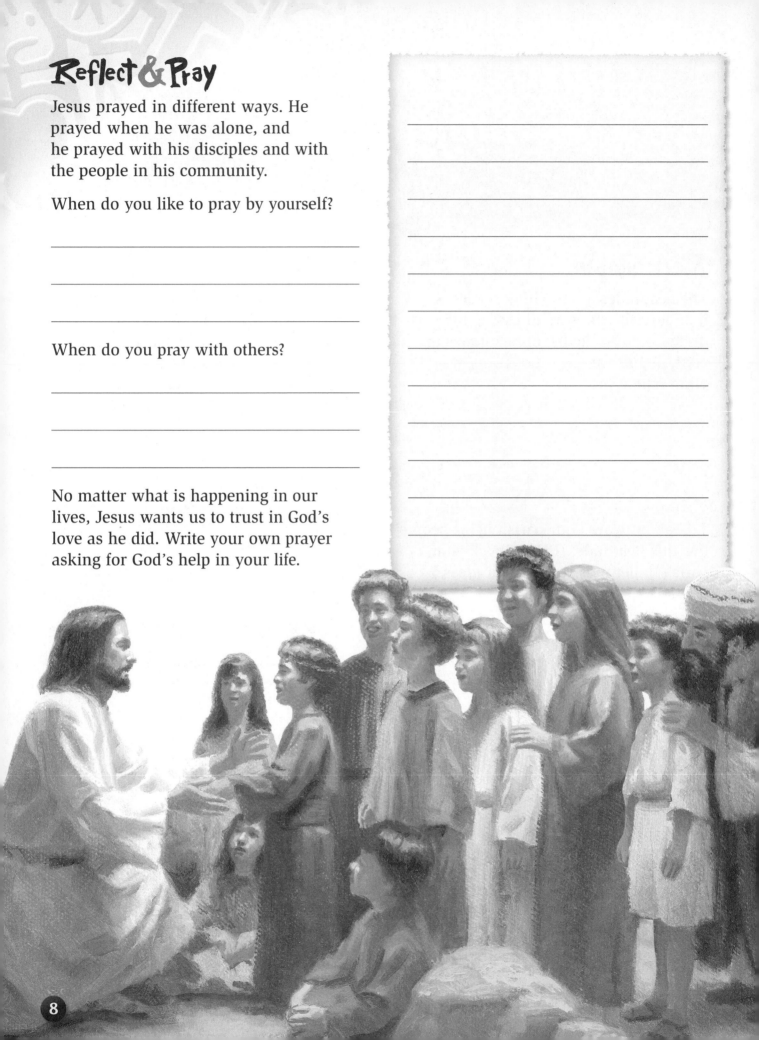

Our Catholic Life

Complete this activity with someone in your family.

Imagine how life would be if all people believed in and shared God's love.

Describe some of the things that would happen:

imagine

in families...

in parishes...

in schools...

in the world...

Sin in Our World

Remember

The editor of a fourth grade newsletter has asked you to answer some letters.

Here are two letters from fourth graders. Write your response for each.

Hi!

There is a new student in my fourth grade class. Everyone makes fun of this student because of the way he talks. I don't make fun of him. I want to tell the other kids to stop, but I don't know how to do this. Can you help me?

Signed,

Confused

Dear Confused,

_____

_____

_____

_____

_____

Hi there!

My sister is so annoying. We argue all the time. She always takes my things without asking. She is never nice to me. I can't help but get mad at her! I know I shouldn't fight, but it's so hard to get along with her. I really need your help.

Signed,

Bothered by Sister

Dear Bothered by Sister,

_____

_____

_____

_____

_____

Key Words

Solve the riddles.

Riddle Word Bank

free will
venial sin
sin
mortal sin
temptation

This is the freedom to decide when and how to act.

What is this?

_____

This is a thought, word, or action against God's law.

What is this?

_____

This is an attraction to choose sin.

What is this?

_____

This is a very serious sin that breaks a person's friendship with God.

What is this?

_____

This is a less serious sin that hurts a person's friendship with God.

What is this?

_____

Reflect & Pray

Saint Francis of Assisi wrote
"It is in giving that we receive,
It is in pardoning that we are pardoned."

What do you think this means?

Turn to the "Prayers and Practices" section in your *We Believe* text. Read the Prayer for Peace. Think about ways the prayer can have meaning for a fourth grader today. Add your own lines to the prayer.

Lord, make me an instrument of your peace:

where there is hatred, _____

_____ ;

where there is injury, _____

_____ ;

where there is doubt, _____

_____ ;

where there is despair, _____

_____ ;

where there is darkness, _____

_____ .

Now say your own Prayer for Peace with family and friends.

Our Catholic Life

As disciples of Jesus, we should live a life that shows that we value and respect all human beings. Sometimes people are afraid to speak out against injustice. Sometimes people are ignored or threatened because of the color of their skin, their nationality, gender, age, or religion.

With a family member, look through the newspaper or on the Internet, and find articles that show examples of injustice.

Prepare a 30-second television advertisement that will call people to work for justice. Use the storyboard to outline your TV spot.

Justice **NOW**

Remember

Conscience works in three ways:

- It works **BEFORE** you make decisions.
- It works **WHILE** you are making decisions.
- It works **AFTER** you have made decisions.

Read this story.

> One morning before school, Amy accidentally knocked Mrs. Harrison's favorite plant off her desk while she was returning a book. The container was smashed to pieces, and the flower was crushed. No one else was in the room at the time, so Amy just took her seat. When Mrs. Harrison came into the room and saw the ruined plant, she asked if anyone knew what had happened. Amy said nothing.

With a partner, take turns interviewing each other. One person takes the part of Amy; the other person takes the part of the interviewer. Ask these questions and write the responses.

- Why didn't you say something right away, Amy?
- How did you feel when the teacher asked about what happened to her plant?
- Looking back now, is there something else you could have done?

_____

_____

_____

_____

_____

_____

_____

_____

Making decisions is a part of everyone's life. Write about a time at school, home, or play where the choice you made showed love for God, yourself, and others.

One time, when I was

_____

_____

_____

_____

_____

_____

_____

Congratulations! You have made the right decision!

Share your story with your class or family.

Reflect & Pray

When we forget God's love and turn away from him, God is always ready to welcome us back as his children. Finish the following prayer.

When I have difficult decisions to make,

help me _____

_____

Loving Father, you will always welcome me back.

When I make a wrong decision at home

or at school, help me _____

_____

Loving Father, you will always welcome me back.

When I have failed to show love for myself as a person made in God's image,

help me _____

_____

Loving Father, you will always welcome me back.

Our Catholic Life

Write the names of three trusted adults in your family, school, parish, and community who have helped you to form a good conscience. Consider them to be "Good Conscience All Stars." Write about them.

Thank each of these people who through their words and actions have helped you to form a good conscience.

My "Good Conscience All-Star" Team

Name _____

Why this person is a "Good Conscience All Star":

_____

_____

Name _____

Why this person is a "Good Conscience All Star":

_____

_____

Name _____

Why this person is a "Good Conscience All Star":

_____

_____

Celebrating Penance and Reconciliation

Remember

Contrition, confession, penance, and absolution are always part of the Sacrament of Penance and Reconciliation. In order to fully participate in this sacrament, you need to know the *Who*, *What*, *When*, *Where*, and *How* of the sacrament's celebration in your parish.

● Who in your parish can forgive sins in God's name?

_____

● What happens during the Sacrament of Penance?

_____

● When is the Sacrament of Penance celebrated in your parish?

_____

● Where is the Sacrament of Penance usually celebrated in your parish?

_____

● How does your parish celebrate Penance?

_____

Clue: If time permits, you might want to use these sources:
    church bulletin
    church visit
    parish staff members
    parish Web site, if one is available.

Compare your findings with others in your class.

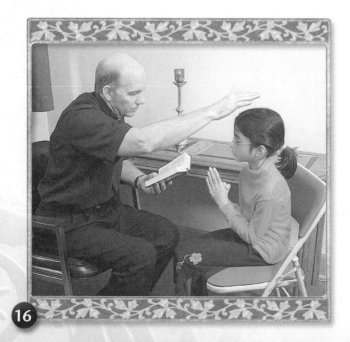

Key Words

Choose a partner and each solve one puzzle on the

WHEEL OF FORGIVENESS

Taking turns, have each player guess one word. All the vowels are already listed for each word.

☐ E ☐ I ☐ E ☐ ☐   **LETTER KEY: T, N, P, N, T**

Clue: a person seeking God's forgiveness in the Sacrament of Penance

A ☐ ☐ O ☐ U ☐ I O ☐   **LETTER KEY: N, B, S, L, T**

Clue: God's forgiveness of sins through the words of the priest

Reflect & Pray

Penance is a sacrament that brings peace and unity. Take some time to think about the following:

What are two ways I can bring peace to the world this week?

_____

_____

_____

What will I do?

_____

_____

After you have put your peace plan into action, report the results of your efforts to the class. Or describe them in the space below.

_____

_____

_____

_____

_____

Share these words with every member of your family today:

"The peace of the Lord be with you."

17

Our Catholic Life

Imagine that you have been appointed to a new position in the government. You are the very first Secretary of Peace and Unity. Your job is to help create unity. You are to advise the president about peaceful ways to solve disagreements between citizens.

Here is the problem you have been given: There is a forest in your neighborhood where birds and deer make their home. It is going to be cut down to make a soccer field. Some people want to keep the forest. Others want a place to play soccer near their homes.

MEMO

TO: The President

FROM: The Secretary of Peace and Unity,

_____
(your name)

DATE: _____
(today's date)

SUBJECT: **My Solution to the Forest Problem**

_____

_____

_____

_____

_____

_____

_____

_____

_____

_____

_____

Learning About God's Law

Remember

You have been asked to teach the Ten Commandments to a group of fourth graders who have never heard of the commandments. Choose three of the commandments in Chapter 8 of your *We Believe* text. Explain them in your own words. Use examples from your school, parish, and home to help the fourth graders understand these commandments. Remember, keep it simple! List the commandments you have chosen and write what you are going to say.

_____

_____

_____

_____

_____

_____

_____

_____

Key Words

Write each of the Key Words on the correct line.

covenant
human rights
Ten Commandments

Remember to keep holy the Lord's Day.
Honor your father and your mother.
You shall not steal.

These are three of the

_____

The right to life
The right to equal treatment
The right to education

These are examples of

_____

God promised to protect his people.

God promised to help his people live in freedom.

The people promised to live as God wanted them to live.

These statements describe a

_____

Reflect & Pray

Describe how you pray.

My special place to pray is

_____

My favorite time of day to pray is

_____

A special person I like to share prayer with is

_____

My favorite prayer to pray is

_____

Complete the sentences. You may use more than one word from the box for each sentence.

television	talking	radio
	CDs	computer	
	video games	noise	

When I prepare to pray, I turn off the

_____

I focus on my conversation with God and stop playing with

_____

I try to reduce as many distractions as I can, such as

_____

Our Catholic Life

Jesus explained the Great Commandment:

"You shall love the Lord, your God, with all your heart, with all your soul, and with all your mind. . . . You shall love your neighbor as yourself."

(Matthew 22:37, 39)

Team up with a partner or a family member to help you answer: How do you live the Great Commandment?

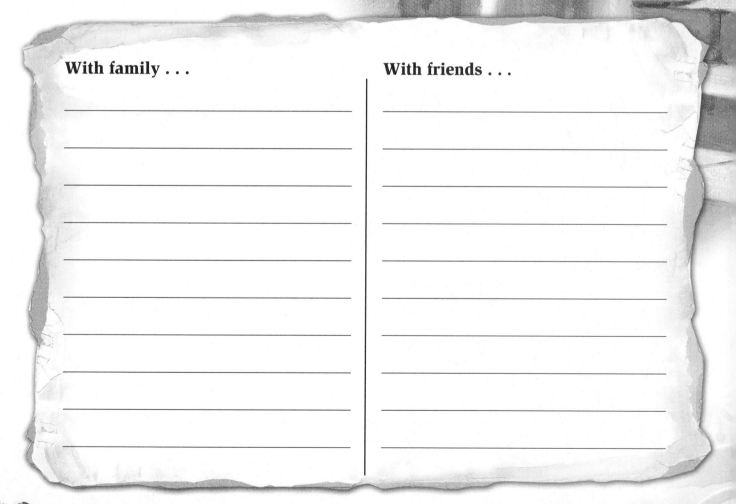

With family . . .

_____

_____

_____

_____

_____

_____

_____

With friends . . .

_____

_____

_____

_____

_____

_____

_____

Act out one way you live out the Great Commandment.

The First Commandment

Remember

We believe in the one true God. Each week we honor the one true God on Sunday, the Lord's Day. One of the ways we worship God each week is by praying the "Holy, Holy, Holy." You can find this prayer on the Prayers and Practices pages in your *We Believe* text.

With the help of a family member, fill in the missing words using this word box.

Lord	glory	hosts
highest	name	Hosanna

Learn this prayer by heart. Pray it with the assembly when you go to Mass.

Holy, Holy, Holy _____

God of _____.

Heaven and earth are full of

your _____.

_____ in the highest.

Blessed is he who comes in

the _____ of the Lord.

Hosanna in the _____.

Key Words

Unscramble the letters to find the word that fits the definition.

giving God thanks and praise

P R O S I W H

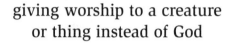

_____

giving worship to a creature or thing instead of God

D I L Y A R O T

_____

listening and talking to God with our minds and hearts

E A P Y R R

_____

Reflect & Pray

God will always help you when you ask. Imagine that you saw this headline on the Internet:

E-Mail God!!!
Will Respond 24 Hours a Day!!!

Write an e-mail to God. Ask him to help you to always place your hope and trust in him.

Address: @ www.webelieveweb.com

Our Catholic Life

Keeping the First Commandment means that we put God first in our lives. This may not always be easy for many of us. We have so many interests and activities that sometimes we might forget God's place in our lives.

Brainstorm ideas for a family or class project to help those in your neighborhood to remember to put God first in their lives. Plan one of the following: a 30-second announcement on local talk radio, or a billboard on a main highway, or a Web site.

Write your ideas for your project here.

The Second Commandment

Remember

We honor God by using his name with respect. Following the Second Commandment also means having a deep respect for all God's children. Therefore, we should use every person's name with respect.

Did you ever name a pet or a favorite toy? If so, you know how important it is to pick just the right name. With a family member or a partner in your class, play the "Name Game."

What is your first name?

_____

How did your family choose your name?

_____

Is it a name that others in your family have had?

_____

What do you like about your name?

_____

Do you also have a nickname?

_____

If so, what do you like about that name?

_____

Key Words

Find these words hidden in the puzzle and circle them.

bless
reverence
psalm
sacred

```
L K A R A K O T R
I B L E S S A E E
Y I A V N O T R L
R I P E P S A L M
O U B R G A E K A
D L I E E C N R J
X H O N O R N A T
O P C C Q E C H I
F I Z E E D H V I
```

Write each word below its meaning.

A song of praise to honor God

_____

Honor, love, and respect

_____

Another word for holy

_____

To dedicate someone or something to God

_____

Reflect & Pray

The psalms are songs of praise to honor the Lord. They express different human emotions, such as love, hope, and joy.

Choose one of these emotions. Write your own psalm about the love, or hope, or joy in your life. Begin each line of your psalm with the letter of the emotion you have chosen.

L _____

O _____

V _____

E _____

H _____

O _____

P _____

E _____

J _____

O _____

Y _____

Note: Your group might want to put together a "Book of Fourth Grade Psalms" for the prayer space.

Our Catholic Life

There are many symbols and practices that remind us that we are in a sacred space when we are at church. One of these is when the priest says, "The peace of the Lord be with you always." We shake the hands of those around us. This is called the Sign of Peace.

Our neighborhood and world are full of places and people who need a "sign of peace." Plan an ad campaign that promotes peace in an area of the world. Use the form below to help you get started.

Where is peace needed?

_____

_____

_____

Why have you chosen this place?

_____

_____

_____

_____

What do you hope will happen when people read or see your ad?

_____

_____

_____

_____

What will your ad look like?

The Third Commandment

Remember

"Remember to keep holy the Lord's Day." Every Sunday we gather to celebrate that Jesus died and rose to save us.

Plan a special Sunday. Use ideas from the suggestion box to fill in "My Sunday Planner."

My Sunday Planner

8:00 AM _____

10:00 AM _____

12:00 PM _____

2:00 PM _____

4:00 PM _____

6:00 PM _____

8:00 PM _____

Suggestion Box

- Rise and praise God for this special day.
- Get ready for Mass.
- Take time to rest.
- Listen carefully to the readings.
- Pray aloud with my family.
- Receive Jesus in the Eucharist.
- Have a "thanks-giving" dinner.
- Draw a picture, write a letter, or write a poem for a sick relative, elderly person or a patient in a children's hospital.
- Discuss reasons why each family member should be thankful this week.
- Plan and go on a special family outing.
- Go to visit other family members or friends.

Key Words

Match the words to their correct definitions.

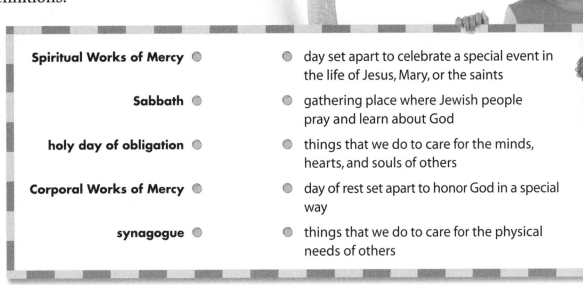

Spiritual Works of Mercy ○   ○ day set apart to celebrate a special event in the life of Jesus, Mary, or the saints

Sabbath ○   ○ gathering place where Jewish people pray and learn about God

holy day of obligation ○   ○ things that we do to care for the minds, hearts, and souls of others

Corporal Works of Mercy ○   ○ day of rest set apart to honor God in a special way

synagogue ○   ○ things that we do to care for the physical needs of others

Reflect & Pray

Complete this activity with the help of your family. Prepare to make your own special prayer space.

You can pray here at any time. In the morning, you can offer God all the things you will do that day. At night, you can thank God for being with you all day. Remember, this is YOUR sacred prayer space.

STEP ONE
Location for your prayer space
☐ kitchen   ☐ living room
☐ hallway   ☐ (other) _____

STEP TWO
Depending on the current season of the liturgical year, choose an appropriately colored covering to be placed on the table or other surface in your prayer space. See the chart below.

Advent and Lent	Purple
Easter	White
Christmas	Gold
Triduum	White (with red)
Ordinary Time	Green

STEP THREE
Place some appropriate items in your prayer space.
(Check the items you have gathered.)
☐ Bible
☐ crucifix
☐ decorations of the season
☐ holy water
☐ prayer notebook
☐ statue or holy card
☐ (other)

Our Catholic Life

No one should wake up hungry or go without proper clothes. Live the Corporal Works of Mercy. As a group, or with your family, plan a way to help people in need.

Who needs our help?

_____

_____

_____

How can we help in our group?

_____

_____

in our parish?

_____

_____

in our neighborhood?

_____

_____

in our world?

_____

_____

Suggestions might be for families to bring a box of cereal or canned good to school or the parish this week. Or family members might clean out a closet and set aside clothes in good condition that are no longer worn. You might research food banks in your neighborhood by looking in telephone or Internet directories.

If you and your group or family follow your plan or use it to make a group plan, describe what happened here.

_____

_____

_____

_____

_____

_____

_____

_____

_____

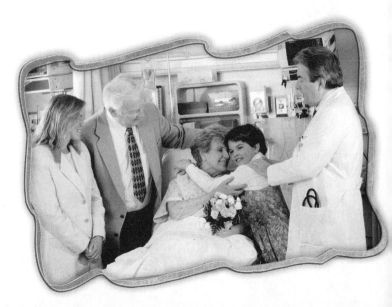

Strengthened by the Eucharist

Remember

There is a saying that "a picture is worth a thousand words." Check Chapter 12 in your *We Believe* text for valuable information about each part of the Mass. Then choose one of the four main parts of the Mass, and design a "MASSterpiece." Include in your drawing any special things that your parish does during that part of the celebration of the Mass.

Key Words

Across

3. the part of the Mass when we listen and respond to God's Word is the Liturgy of the _____

5. the Church's greatest prayer of praise and thanksgiving to God is the _____ prayer

6. the community of people gathered to worship in the name of Jesus Christ

7. the part of the Eucharistic Prayer when, by the power of the Holy Spirit and through the words and actions of the priest, the bread and wine become the Body and Blood of Christ

Down

1. a talk given by the priest or deacon that helps us to understand the readings and to grow as faithful followers of Jesus

2. the part of the Mass in which the Death and Resurrection of Christ are made present again is the Liturgy of the _____

4. the celebration of the Eucharist

Reflect & Pray

One of the Introductory Rites is the penitential rite. We pray and ask for God's forgiveness. With a partner, read aloud this part of the prayer:

I confess to almighty God
and to you, my brothers and sisters,
that I have greatly sinned,
in my thoughts and in my words,
in what I have done
and in what I have failed to do.

Think of things that people may fail to do at home, at school, and at play. Write a prayer to help them turn their "failures" into "success stories."

Our Catholic Life

Holy Communion makes the life of God stronger in us.

Think of what we need to nourish our bodies so that we grow strong. On the plate write or draw some foods that make a nutritious meal. ➡

In the same way, our spirit needs nourishment to grow and develop. How are we spiritually nourished each week at Mass?

Write the types of spiritual nourishment you receive. ⬇

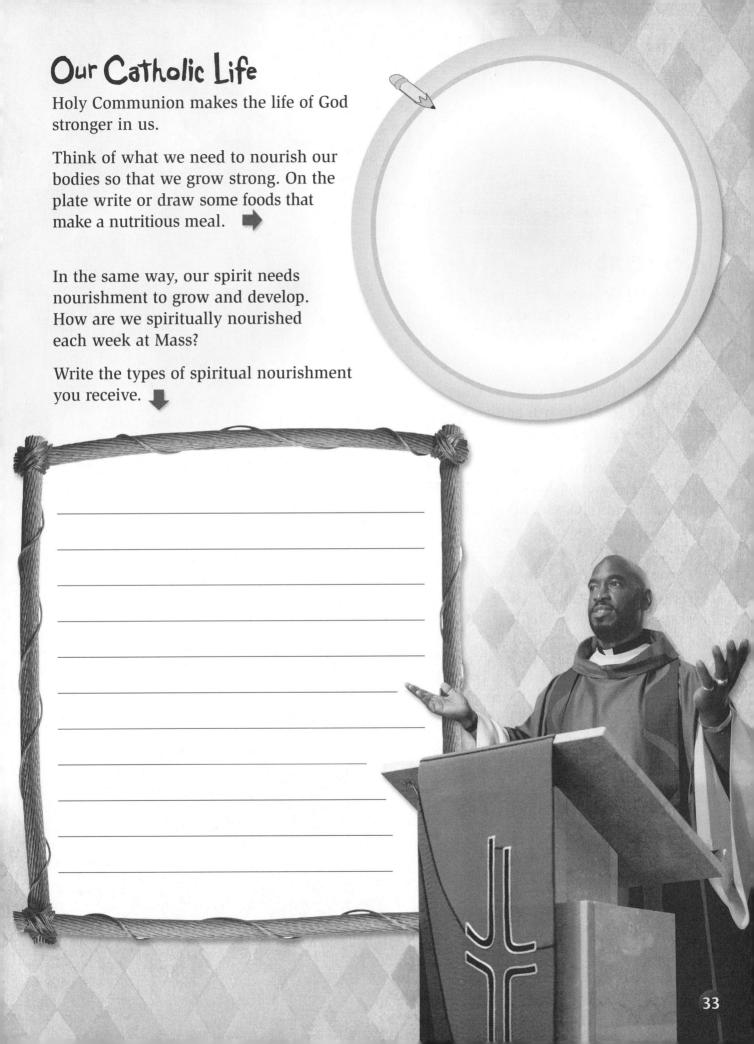

The Fourth Commandment

Remember

The Fourth Commandment is "Honor your father and your mother." It teaches us to appreciate and obey our parents and our guardians.

Read the following situations. Then for each, write a way fourth graders can live out the Fourth Commandment.

Sam's parents have asked him to come home directly from school every day this week to spend time with his grandmother who is visiting. Today, Sam's friend, Carlos, invites him over after school to see his new puppy. Sam really wants to go to Carlos's house. What should Sam do?

_____

_____

_____

_____

_____

_____

Late one night, Jane realizes that she needs more poster paint to finish her school project for tomorrow morning's class. She really wants to do a good job on the project, so she is anxious to get the materials. Jane's mother has offered to go out and get her the needed paints even though there is a heavy rain storm. How can Jane show appreciation to her mother?

_____

_____

_____

_____

_____

Every Christian family is called to be a domestic church—a "church in the home." Complete the word puzzle below with ideas for helping your family to live as the domestic church. Each answer must start with the appropriate letter. Three are already done for you.

D_____

Open our doors and welcome friends.

Make peace with brothers and sisters.

Every day, say grace at meals.

S_____

T_____

I_____

C_____

Reflect & Pray

A litany is made up of a number of prayer requests, usually followed by the same response.

Complete this litany for leaders.

Litany for Leaders

Prayer Leader: We value and listen with respect to all those who help us to see God's will. Let us pray for all of those who lead us.

You: For the leaders of our Church— our teachers, priests, bishops, and the Holy Father. Help them to

_____

_____

All: Lord, bless those who lead and serve us.

You: For leaders in our towns and cities. Help them to

_____

_____

All: Lord, bless those who lead and serve us.

You: For the heads of families everywhere. Help them to

_____

_____

All: Lord, bless those who lead and serve us.

You might want to combine your requests with other members of your class. Use it for a prayer service or Mass.

Our Catholic Life

Conduct a survey on what it means to be a good parent or guardian in the world today.

Ask several people who are parents or guardians of school age children (neighbors, teachers, relatives, your own parents or guardians) the following two questions. Record their responses.

What is the most important part of being a parent or guardian?

_____

_____

_____

_____

_____

How has your role changed as your child/children have gotten older?

_____

_____

_____

_____

_____

Share the results of your survey.

The Fifth Commandment

Remember

Over the next four days, record your attitudes about the gift of life. Write two or three sentences each day.

Here are some questions to think about before you write:

- How did I lead a healthy life today?

- How did I help someone in need today?

- How have my actions today shown respect for all life?

Share your ideas with your family.

Day 1

Day 2

Day 3

Day 4

Key Words

Human dignity makes us someone, not something.

Fill in the blanks to complete these statements about human dignity. Use the words in the box.

choices	image
worth	equal
	think

Human dignity is the value and

_____ each person

has from being created

in God's _____ and

likeness. This gift gives us the

ability to _____, to

make _____, and to

love. Human dignity makes us

all _____ with one

another.

Reflect & Pray

In his great love, God calls all those who have sinned to come back to him. We believe that God will show mercy and love to those who are truly sorry.

Take this Good News and spread it to all your family members. Use this Mass prayer as an "echo prayer" before your next family meal.

Lord, have mercy.   (echo)

Christ, have mercy. (echo)

Lord, have mercy.   (echo)

Draw a picture of a family sharing a meal together.

Our Catholic Life

The Church community works toward peace by helping people:

- have things they need to live

- feel safe and free to talk to one another

- respect the dignity of individuals and societies

- follow Jesus' command to love others as he loves us.

How does your parish work for peace? Record the ways here.

How does your diocese work for peace? Record the ways here.

 How does the worldwide Church work for peace? With a family member, teacher, or catechist, visit the Vatican Web site (www.vatican.net) and the U.S. Conference of Catholic Bishops Web site (www.usccb.org). Record what you found in this space.

From:

Subject: Ways the worldwide Church works for peace

The Sixth Commandment

Remember

There are many qualities that make up a good friend. With a partner or family member, talk about these qualities. Make up a "Top Ten" list of what you believe it takes to make a good, faithful, and valued friend. Share your list with the rest of the class.

Top Ten Qualities of a Good Friend

#10 _____

#9 _____

#8 _____

#7 _____

#6 _____

#5 _____

#4 _____

#3 _____

#2 _____

#1 _____

Are the following statements TRUE or FALSE? If they are FALSE, change them to make them TRUE.

False A virtue is a ~~bad~~ *good* habit.

_____ Chastity is a virtue.

_____ A virtue helps us to act according to God's love for us.

_____ Chastity is the virtue by which we use our human sexuality in a responsible and faithful way.

_____ Through our Confirmation, we are called to live by the virtue of chastity.

Reflect & Pray

Jesus said, "I call you friend."

Write a verse or poem for a greeting card that could be sent to a good friend. Include some reasons why friendships stay strong.

Draw pictures or cut out and paste pictures on your card to show ways friends love and care for each other.

Our Catholic Life

In the Sacrament of Matrimony, the husband and wife make a vow to each other. They promise to be faithful or true to each other for the rest of their lives.

Interview a married couple—an aunt and uncle, your neighbors, or your parents or guardians. Ask the couple to share a memory about their life together. Ask them to share memories about their friendship with one another.

Ask what advice they would give to others to help them to remain good, faithful, and true friends.

Record your interview. Then decorate the frame around your interview.

You might want to share with your class what you learned about forming and keeping a strong, faithful relationship.

The Seventh Commandment

Remember

Every decision we make affects others in some way.

Read the following situations. Draw a line from each action on the left to its consequence on the right.

Your friend is going away on a trip. He asked you to take care of his plants for the week. You agreed.

Action: You don't water the plants.

Action: Each day you water the plants.

Consequence: Your grateful friend gives you a souvenir from his trip.

Consequence: Your friend is upset about his plants and says you did not keep your promise.

You forgot to bring your lunch money again. You know that your friend, Jenny, always keeps her money in her desk.

Action: Jenny has lent you lunch money before, and you have always paid her back. So you ask Jenny for $1.50.

Action: You take the money from Jenny's desk. You tell yourself you'll return it whenever you can.

Consequence: Jenny tells you she will lend you the money and asks that you pay her back tomorrow.

Consequence: Jenny tells the teacher that her money is missing. The teacher waits for someone to confess to taking it.

Write a possible action and consequence for the following.

You were told not to play ball in the house. You see a large beach ball in the living room. You think, "Oh, what could this hurt?"

Action: _____   **Consequence:** _____

_____   _____

Key Word

Fill in the following sections to describe the job for a "steward of creation."

Must have these qualities: _____

_____

Should be able to: _____

_____

Will be responsible for:_____

_____

Must work from _____ to _____

Employment benefits are: _____

_____

Now write a classified ad for this job for your local paper. (You can only use 20 words or less.)

FULL TIME
Steward of Creation

_____

_____

_____

_____

_____

Reflect & Pray

Jesus showed mercy to people, especially those who were poor. Jesus expects his disciples to share and to be generous toward others. We pray for the poor; we must also respond to their needs.

Think about the needs of those who are poor. Write a prayer that will inspire others to pray and help these people.

Now silently pray your prayer.

44

Our Catholic Life

Complete this activity with a family member or a partner.

In newspapers or on the Internet, find a news article about people who are in need (food, clean water, medicine, shelter), or people who are suffering and need freedom from war.

After reading the article, make up a quiz about the situation. Write true or false questions or multiple choice. Then give your quiz to someone else to complete. See how he or she does!

The _____ Quiz

by _____

_____

_____

_____

_____

_____

_____

_____

Person who took the quiz _____

Number of questions answered correctly _____

HOLY FAMILY CHURCH
CLOTHING DRIVE

KEEP OFF
THE
GRASS

The Eighth Commandment

Remember

Saint Paul wrote many letters to followers of Jesus offering them encouragement and talking about ways they could live as Christians.

Imagine that Saint Paul is writing to Christians in your town today about ways to live the Eighth Commandment. Write what you think he would say.

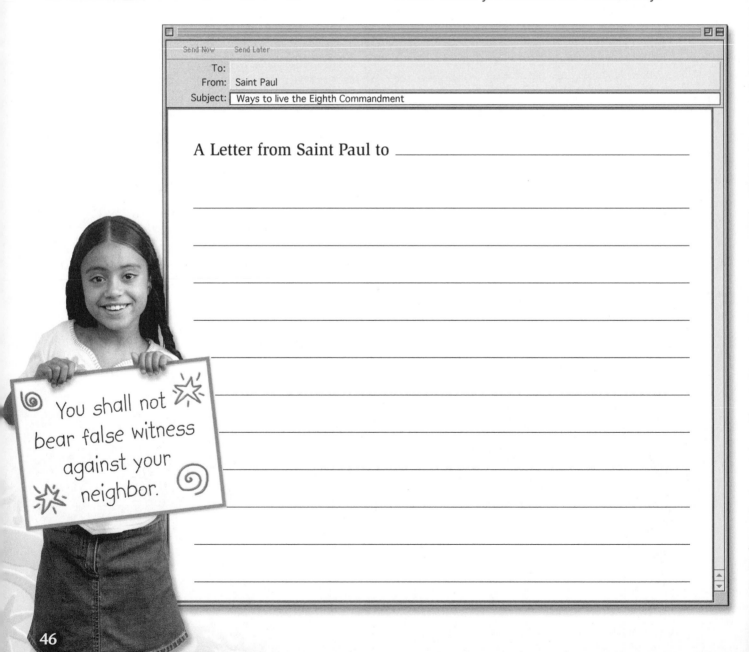

Send Now   Send Later

To:
From: Saint Paul
Subject: Ways to live the Eighth Commandment

A Letter from Saint Paul to _____

_____

_____

_____

_____

_____

_____

_____

_____

You shall not bear false witness against your neighbor.

Key Words

Explain what is the same or what is different between a witness and a martyr.

_____

_____

_____

_____

_____

_____

_____

Think about events that are happening right now in our world. Where do you see witnesses? Where do you see martyrs?

Reflect & Pray

We need to ask the Holy Spirit for help and guidance each day. To help remember this, start each week by turning to the Holy Spirit for help. Here are some ideas:

- Light a red "Holy Spirit" candle at Sunday dinner each week.

- Read the "Prayer to the Holy Spirit." This is in the Prayers and Practices section of your *We Believe* text. Learn this prayer by heart.

- Say the following prayer before or after going to Mass: "Holy Spirit, guide my family and me each day this week."

- Add your own ideas for seeking the Holy Spirit's help.

_____

_____

_____

_____

_____

_____

_____

_____

_____

_____

Circle one idea that you will try to do this week.

Our Catholic Life

Write the name of one person you know who fits in each category below. Then in the star, write words that describe what is good and positive about that person.

Be sure that the words you use are respectful of each person. Share your "stars" with a member of your class or family. Then think about the words others might use to describe you.

Someone in my family ○ · · · ·

_____

Someone in my school ○ · · · ·

_____

Someone in my parish ○ · · · · · · · · · ·

_____

· · · ○ **Someone who is my friend**

_____

Someone I like to watch on TV ○ · · · ·

_____

Someone I hear good things about in the news ○ · · · · · · · ·

_____

The Ninth Commandment

Remember

Read the following situations. Fill in the blanks to show possible ways that people act in positive or negative ways.

This week, remember to act on your feelings in a positive way.

1. A friend makes fun of your new haircut.

It can be tempting to _____.

A more positive way to respond is _____.

2. Your mom accidentally throws away your school papers.

It can be tempting to _____.

A more positive way to respond is _____.

3. Someone jumps in front of you in line at the movies.

It can be tempting to _____.

A more positive way to respond is _____.

4. A younger brother or sister borrows your bicycle without asking.

It can be tempting to _____.

A more positive way to respond is _____.

5. On your way to play ball, you see a neighbor struggling with heavy bags.

It can be tempting to _____.

A more positive way to respond is _____.

Key Words

Read the mini-stories. Decide whether the missing word is **covet** or **modesty**.

Henry has a new video game system. It is one that John has wanted for a long time. John thinks to himself that he must remember to be happy for Henry. But John would like to have the system for himself. John must

not _____ his friend's new game.

Carole was invited to a school dance, so she needed a special outfit. She tried on a very short, very tight dress that the woman at the department store said was very popular. Carole decides not to buy the dress because the outfit would not show that she has

a sense of _____.

Reflect & Pray

Mary, the Mother of Jesus, wants us to live as devoted children of God. We can pray to Mary to intercede, or ask, God to help us.

Fill out the "Mary Prayer Card."

Is there a special place in your parish devoted to Mary? It might be a beautiful statue or an outside grotto. You can also make a special space for Mary in your home. Go to one of these special places and offer your prayer to Mary. Also pray the Hail Mary often to honor Mary, the Mother of Jesus.

Mary, show us ways to speak and act with a pure heart.
With our friends, help us
With our families, help us
Your name

Our Catholic Life

Design the home page of a Web site that is urging everyone to follow the Ninth Commandment. Review Chapter 22 in your *We Believe* text to decide what visuals you will draw, the navigation bar you will use, and the Scripture you will quote.

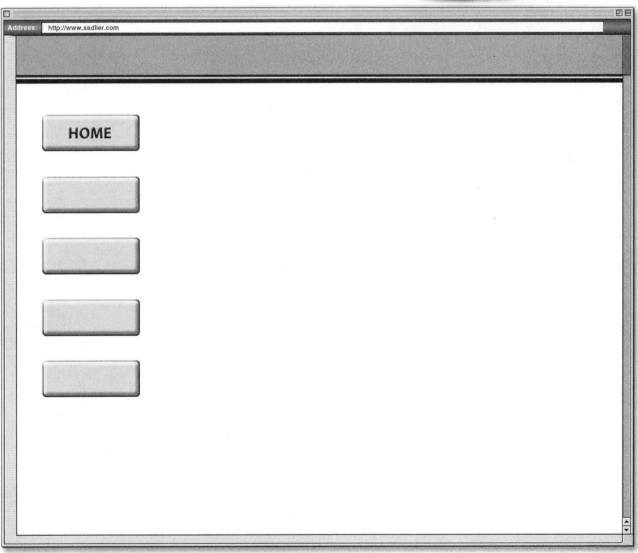

Share your home page with a friend or family member. Describe why you think visitors will be inspired to follow the Ninth Commandment after they view your site. Write some reasons here:

_____

_____

_____

_____

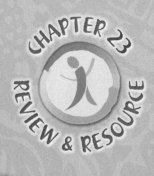

The Tenth Commandment

Remember

Try this "5-Minute Spiritual Exercise Program." You can complete this activity by yourself or with a family member or friend.

Find a space where you can move your arms and legs without bumping into anything. Stand with your feet slightly apart.

Warm-Up — Clear your mind of all wishful thoughts for the things that others have.

Step 1 — Stretch your arms as far as you can. Then slowly bring them together. Say, "We are called to have generous hearts."

Step 2 — Reach your arms to heaven as you grow in faith. Say, "Jesus teaches us to trust in God above all things." Repeat 3 times.

Step 3 — Form a circle with your arms in front of you. Bring your hands together. Say, "Depending upon God brings happiness."

Step 4 — Now spread your arms out with your palms facing up. Say, "Jesus, teach us that God's law is love."

Cool Down — Breathe deeply and slowly. Think of all the things and people for which you are thankful.

Glory to You, Lord

Key Words

Write the correct word to answer each riddle.

> greed
> poor in spirit
> envy

I depend on God completely.

I find joy in the simple things of life.

Trust, openness, and joy are the words that describe me.

Who am I?

_____

I can make you forget what is really important in life.

I am a strong feeling of wanting to own things.

I am an excessive desire to have material goods.

Who am I?

_____

I am never happy for the success of other people.

I can lead to taking what is not mine.

I am a feeling of sadness when someone else has what I want.

Who am I?

_____

Reflect & Pray

Each day the Lord blesses us in many ways. At the end of each day this week, write down one way your life has been blessed by God.

Blessed By God

MONDAY————————

TUESDAY————————

WEDNESDAY————————

THURSDAY————————

FRIDAY————————

SATURDAY————————

SUNDAY————————

At the end of the week, decorate the space around your writing. Pray: "Thank you, generous God, for all your gifts. Amen."

Our Catholic Life

Have you ever seen messages as television commercials?

The newest sneakers!

The greatest amusement park!

The best place in town to eat!

The brightest smile!

Write a television commercial advertising something that all people really do need. Tell how it will improve life and make us better people.

Act out your commercial for a partner or family member. See if they "buy" what you are trying to "sell."

We Grow in Holiness

Remember

We grow in holiness when we believe in Jesus, live as Jesus did, work for peace and justice, pray, and celebrate the sacraments.

Imagine you are a newspaper reporter for the "Good News Gazette." You have been assigned to interview your favorite saint. The title of your article is "What It Means To Be Holy." Write the questions you would ask in your interview.

Ask a partner or family member to answer your questions as he or she thinks your saint would answer them.

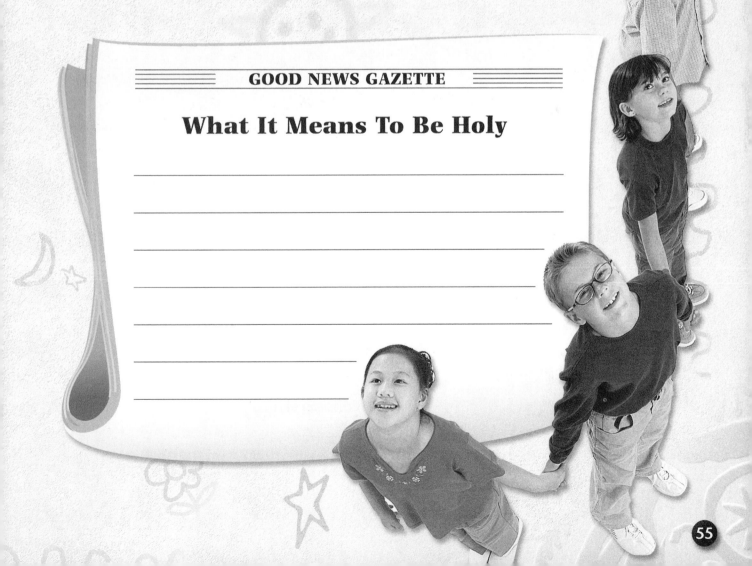

GOOD NEWS GAZETTE

What It Means To Be Holy

_____

_____

_____

_____

_____

_____

_____

Key Words

In each blank, write the **Key Word** that is related to the ideas branching out from the sun design.

> liturgy
> gifts of the Holy Spirit
> sacrament
> fruits of the Holy Spirit

Holy Orders
Confirmation
Matrimony
Eucharist
Penance
Baptism
Anointing the Sick

courage
knowledge
understanding
wisdom
right judgment
reverence
wonder & awe

gentleness
self-control
patience
love
joy
generosity
peace
kindness
faithfulness

public prayer
celebration of the sacraments
celebration of Mass
gathering to pray
together in Christ's name
the Body of Christ on earth
praise God for blessings

Reflect & Pray

Gestures are an important part of praying.

By yourself or with a partner, think of some gestures that you could use when praying the Our Father. Fill in the blanks by replacing the prayer words with your gestures.

Our Father, who art in _____,

hallowed be thy name;

thy _____ come;

thy will be done on _____

as it is in _____.

Give us this day our daily _____;

and forgive us our trespasses as we

forgive those who trespass against us;

and _____ us not into

temptation, but deliver us from evil.

_____

You might want to also pray the Our Father in sign language.

Ask a teacher, family member, or friend who knows sign language.

Find a book on sign language in the library to learn some of the words from the Our Father.

Our Catholic Life

Write a story titled "A Day in the Life of a Fourth Grader." In your story, tell how the gifts of the Holy Spirit can help you in everyday situations.

_____

_____

_____

_____

_____

_____

_____

_____

_____

_____

_____

_____

_____

_____

Pray a prayer of thanksgiving to the Holy Spirit for giving you guidance each day.

We Are the Church

Remember

A parish is a community of believers who worship and work together. What does it take to "build" a parish?

Fill in these building blocks to form your parish's foundation. Put your answers on the labeled blocks.

- Name three people who work in your parish. Write their names in building blocks A, B, and C.

- Name four ministries in which people in your parish can get involved. Write these ministries in building blocks D, E, F, and G.

- Name two ways your parish serves those who are in need. Write these in building blocks H, and I.

- Name two ways your parish lets people know when to come together for Mass and the sacraments. Write these ways in building blocks J and K.

- Write the name of your parish in building block L.

A

B

C

D

E

F

G

H

I

J

K

L

Key Words

Using the **Key Words** from this chapter, complete the puzzle.

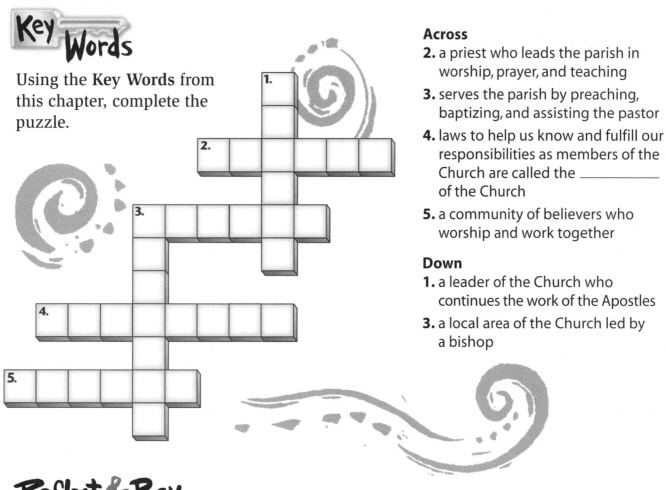

Across

2. a priest who leads the parish in worship, prayer, and teaching

3. serves the parish by preaching, baptizing, and assisting the pastor

4. laws to help us know and fulfill our responsibilities as members of the Church are called the _____ of the Church

5. a community of believers who worship and work together

Down

1. a leader of the Church who continues the work of the Apostles

3. a local area of the Church led by a bishop

Reflect & Pray

Sometimes people write songs as signs of love. Think about what it means to be a sign of Jesus in our world today.

Work with a family member or friend. Write a song that includes some of your ideas.

When you have finished writing your verses, share your song with your class.

Our Catholic Life

Every person needs to take an active role in living as a member of the Church.

Complete this role-play activity with members of your family or friends. Work in groups of four. Assign each person a number from one to four.

- Whoever has 1 is the survey taker.
- Whoever has 2 is a teenager.
- Whoever has 3 is a fourth grader.
- Whoever has 4 is an adult family member.

Within your group, the survey taker asks each of the other three this question:

What can you do to take a more active role in the Church?

Write each person's response.

teenager: _____

_____

_____

fourth grader: _____

_____

_____

adult: _____

_____

_____

How are the responses different?

_____

_____

_____

_____

What will you do to take a more active role in the Church this week?

_____

_____

_____

_____

Caring For Our Community
Catholic Diocese of Gary
and
Northwest Indiana Habitat for Humanity

CATHOLIC DIOCESE OF GARY AND NWI Habitat for Humanity

We Are Called to Discipleship

Remember

Long ago when knights defended their kingdoms, they would carry colorful shields.

Armed with faith, hope, and love, we live as Jesus taught us to. Decorate the shields for the three theological virtues. Use the examples from the chapter to help you.

Faith

Hope

Love

Key Words

Fill in the missing letters.

The theological virtues are gifts from God. They bring us closer to God. They help us to want to be with God forever. They are

> F a _ t h
> H o p _
> L o _ e

The Cardinal Virtues guide our minds and actions to lead a good life. They are

> P _ u d e n c e
> J u _ t i c e
> F o r t i t _ d e
> _ e m p e r a n c e

Write each missing letter on the blanks below. Unscramble the letters to spell an important word in this chapter.

___ ___ ___ ___ ___ ___ ___

Reflect & Pray

Read this prayer and fill in the blanks.

Dear God, guide my mind and actions to lead a good life. Thank you, Lord, for the cardinal virtues: prudence, justice, fortitude, and temperance.

Help me give to you, my friends, and family what is rightfully theirs.

Give me the virtue of

_____.

Help me to act bravely in these fearful and troubled times in our world.

Give me the virtue of

_____.

Help me direct my actions toward what is good in my school, home, and country.

Give me the virtue of

_____.

Help me keep my desires under control. As I grow older, help me to balance my use of material goods.

Give me the virtue of

_____.

Pray your prayer. Pause after each line to think about what it means to you.

Our Catholic Life

Jesus said, "I am the light of the world" (John 8:12). When we accept God's gifts and share our gifts for the good of others, we are a part of that light in the world.

Name ways that you can be a light to others in your school, home, and parish. Color and decorate each candle.

School

Home

Parish

Vice President Publications, Sadlier
Rosemary K. Calicchio

Executive Director of Catechetics
Carole M. Eipers, D.Min.

Director of Research and Planning
Melissa D. Gibbons

Product Developer
Lee Hlavacek

Editorial Director
Blake Bergen

Supervising Editor
Mary Ann Trevaskiss

Senior Editor
Maureen Gallo

Vice President, Publishing Operations
Deborah Jones

Creative Director
Vince Gallo

Photo Editor
Jim Saylor

Acknowledgments
Excerpts from the English translation of *The Roman Missal* © 2010, International Committee on English in the Liturgy, Inc. All rights reserved.

Scripture excerpts are taken from the *New American Bible with Revised New Testament and Psalms.* Copyright © 1991, 1986, 1970 Confraternity of Christian Doctrine, Inc., Washington, D.C. Used with permission. All rights reserved. No part of the *New American Bible* may be reproduced by any means without permission in writing from the copyright owner.

Excerpts from the English translation of the *Catechism of the Catholic Church* for the United States of America. Copyright © 1994, United States Catholic Conference, Inc.—Libreria Editrice Vaticana. English translation of the *Catechism of the Catholic Church: Modifications from the Editio Typica.* Copyright © 1997, United States Catholic Conference, Inc.—Libreria Editrice Vaticana. Used with permission.

English translation of the Our Father and *Sanctus/Benedictus* by the International Consultation on English Texts. (ICET)

Photo Credits
Cover Photography: Getty Images: *Bible, lighthouse,* Ken Karp: *children.* Lori Berkowitz: 14 *left & center.* Karen Callaway: 16, 33, 60 *center.* Corbis/Rolf Bruderer: 17, 24, David Samuel Robbins: 26; Claudia Kunin: 42 *far left;* Rob Lewine: 42 *center right;* Steve Chenn: 42 *couple with oar;* Tom & Dee Ann McCarthy: 42 *far right;* Jon Feingersh: 51. Corbis Sygma/Baldev: 12. Neal Farris: 5, 27, 28, 29, 40, 54 *top,* 55, 60 *bottom,* 61. Getty Images: 14 *right,* 22, 30, 34, 36, 41 *top & center,* 52. Index Stock Imagery/Zephyr Picture: 42 *Hispanic family;* Stewart Cohen: 42 *center left;* Frank Conaway: 42 *African-American couple;* Diaphor Agency: 54 *inset.* Ken Karp: 10, 25, 31, 46, 54 *bottom.* Dick McLernon: 42 *bride & groom.* PhotoEdit/David Young-Wolff: 42 *frames on mantle.* Reuters/Jose Miguel Gomez: 47.

Illustrator Credits
Cover Design: Kevin Ghiglione. Joe Boddy: 5 *path,* 9, 58. Nan Brooks: 50. Janet Broxon: 23. Jim Carroll: 13 *girl.* Penny Carter: 43–45. Ellis Chapell: 29 *notebook and pencil.* Anne Cook: 46 *flowers,* 47 *border.* Jeff Fitz-Maurice: 59 *globe.* Nick Harris: 19. Mary Haverfield: *left border.* Lydia Hess: 25–27. Marilee Heyer: 20. W. B. Johnston: 30 *right,* 38, 55 *background,* 56. Ken Joudrey: 10. Jared Lee: 15. Robert LoGrippo: 7. Francisco Ordaz: 4, 8, 13 *sky,* 21, 36. Donna Perrone: 39 *people.* Gary Philips: 37. Mike Radencich: 28, 29 *ribbon,* 30 *left.* Molly Scanlon: 54 *television,* 55 *newspaper.* J. W. Stewart: 61 *background,* 62, 63 *bottom.* Sally Vitsky: 49. Amanda Warren: 12.